After Midnight *Jazz*

Wise Publications
London/New York/Paris/Sydney/Copenhagen/Madrid

Exclusive Distributors:
Music Sales Limited
8-9 Frith Street,
London W1V 5TZ, England.
Music Sales Pty Limited
120 Rothschild Avenue,
Rosebery, NSW 2018,
Australia.

Order No. AM951753
ISBN 0-7119-7204-4
This book © Copyright 1998 by Wise Publications

New music engravings by MSS Music Publishing and Paul Ewers Music Design

Cover design by Pearce Marchbank Studio, London
Front cover image from an original photograph
from the Telegraph Colour Library

Printed in Great Britain by
Printwise (Haverhill) Limited, Suffolk.

Your Guarantee of Quality

As publishers, we strive to produce every book to the
highest commercial standards.
This book has been carefully designed to minimise awkward
page turns and to make playing from it a real pleasure.
Particular care has been given to specifying acid-free,
neutral-sized paper made from pulps which have not been
elemental chlorine bleached. This pulp is from farmed
sustainable forests and was produced with special regard
for the environment.
Throughout, the printing and binding have been planned
to ensure a sturdy, attractive publication which should
give years of enjoyment.
If your copy fails to meet our high standards,
please inform us and we will gladly replace it.

Music Sales' complete catalogue describes thousands of titles
and is available in full colour sections by subject, direct from
Music Sales Limited. Please state your areas of interest and
send a cheque/postal order for £1.50 for postage to:
Music Sales Limited, Newmarket Road,
Bury St. Edmunds, Suffolk IP33 3YB.

Be Mine Tonight (*Noche De Ronda*)

English Lyric by Sunny Skylar
Music by Maria Teresa Lara

hold you near.

Chorus

See the set - ting sun, the eve - ning's just be - gun and love is in the air; Be mine to - night; At a time like this, would you re - fuse the

sff

mp-mf

5

kiss I'm beg - ging you to share, _____ be

mine to - - - night. _____ Pro - mise this, my

own, be - fore the night has flown, you'll tell me that you care; _____

— And hold me tight; _____

Black Coffee

Words & Music by Paul Francis Webster & Sonny Burke

Very slow and bluesy

Girl version: **I'm**

feel - in' might - y lone - some, have - n't slept a wink, I
feel - in' might - y lone - some, have - n't slept a wink, I

walk the floor and watch the door and in be - tween I drink black
walk the floor and watch the door and in be - tween I drink black

cof - fee.
cof - fee.

Love's a hand - me - down
Since my gal went a -

Georgia On My Mind

Words by Stuart Gorrell
Music by Hoagy Carmichael

Slowly

Mel- o -dies bring mem-or-ies that lin - ger in my heart,_____

Make me think of Geor - gia, Why did we ev - er part?_____

Some sweet day when blos-soms fall and all the world's a song,_____

moon-light through the pines._____ Oth-er arms reach out to me;

Oth-er eyes smile ten-der - ly;___ Still in peace-ful dreams I see the road leads back to

you,_____ Geor-gia,___ Geor-gia,___ no peace I find, Just an

old sweet song keeps Geor-gia on my mind._____ mind.

Goodnight Sweetheart

Words & Music by Ray Noble, Jimmy Campbell & Reg Connelly

Moderato (with rhythmic feeling)

vain re - gret, _____ That made us both un - hap - py.
sil - ver lined _____ with sun - ny days in plen - ty.

CHORUS

Good - night, Sweet-heart, All my pray'rs are for you, Good - night

Sweet-heart, I'll be watch-ing o'er you, Tears and part - ing may

make us for - lorn _____ But with the dawn, _____ A new day is born _____

How Insensitive

Music by Antonio Carlos Jobim. Original Lyrics by Vinicius De Moraes.
English Lyrics by Norman Gimbel

I'm Old Fashioned

Music by Jerome Kern
Words by Johnny Mercer

saint,_____ I'm the type that they class-i-fy as

quaint._____

Refrain *(liltingly)*

I'm old fash-ioned, I love the moon-light, I

love the old fash-ioned things;_____ The

I'm Beginning To See The Light

Words & Music by Harry James, Duke Ellington, Johnny Hodges & Don George

af - ter - glow, __ or can - dle - light on the mis - tle - toe, __ but now when you turn the lamp down low __ I'm be - gin - ning to see the light. __ Used to ram - ble through the park __ sha - dow box - ing in the dark __ then you came and

caused a spark, ___ that's a four a - larm fire ___ now. _____ I

nev - er made love by lan - tern shine, ___ I nev - er saw rain - bows

in my wine, ___ but now that your lips are burn - ing mine, ___ I'm be -

gin - ning to see the light. ___ I _____

In The Still Of The Night

Words & Music by Cole Porter

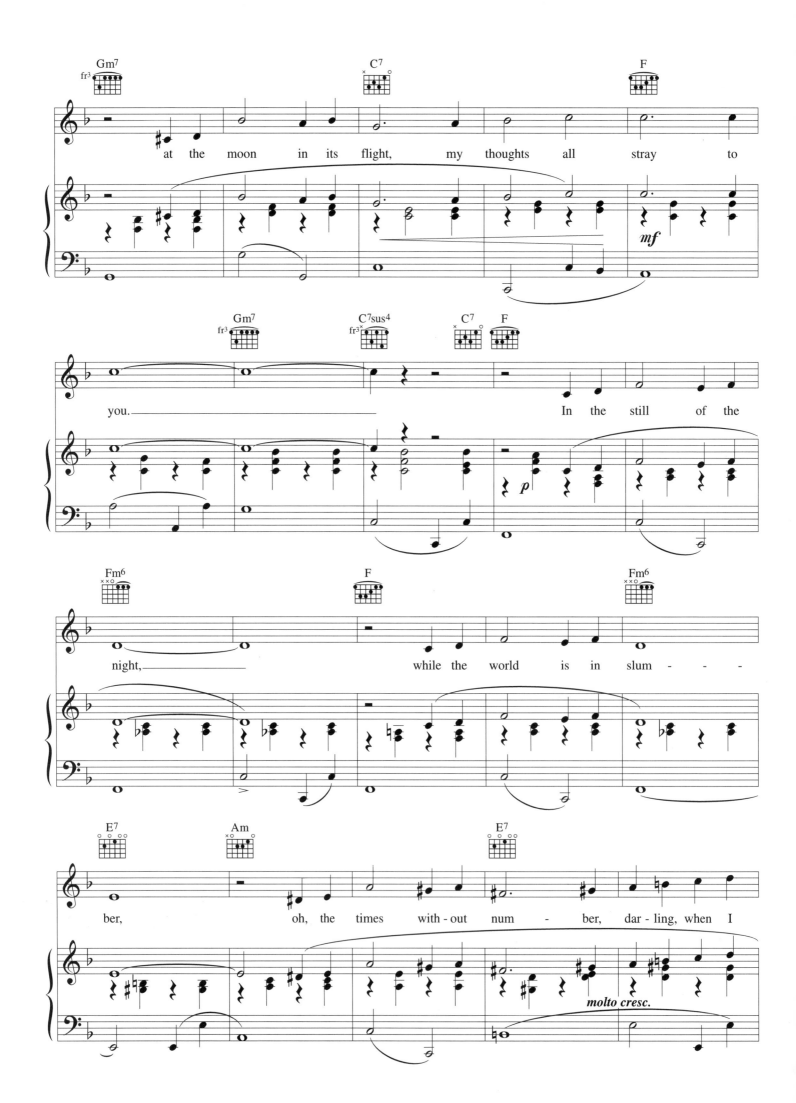

In The Wee Small Hours Of The Morning

Words by Bob Hilliard
Music by David Mann

Killing Me Softly With His Song

Words by Norman Gimbel
Music by Charles Fox

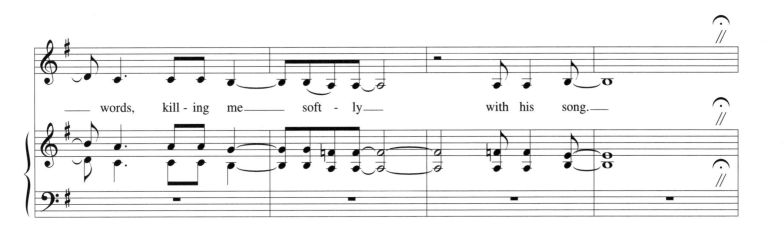

words, kill - ing me soft - ly with his song.

N.C.

8 bars rhythm

1. I heard he sang a good song,
(Verse 2 see block lyric)

I heard he had a smile, and so I came

to see him and lis - ten for a while,

and there he was,— this young boy, a strang-er to— my eyes.—

Em   Am   D

Spoken:

Strum-ming my pain— with his fin - gers,— (one time) sing-ing my life— with his words,.

G   Em   A

Spoken:

— (two times) kill - ing me soft - ly with his— song, kill - ing me soft -

D   C   G

- ly with his— song, tell-ing my whole— life with his—

words,   kill - ing me   soft - ly   with his   song.

Oh_____   oh_____

_____   la la la_____   la la_____   la   woh_____

Repeat ad lib. to fade

Verse 2:
I felt all flushed with fever,
Embarrassed by the crowd,
I felt he found my letters
And read each one out loud,
I prayed that he would finish
But he just kept right on…

Lullaby Of Birdland

Music by George Shearing
Words by George David Weiss

Love Me Tonight

Music by L. Pilat & M. Panzeri. Original Lyrics by D. Pace.
English Lyrics by Barry Mason

hold and I feel such a long way from home;
hard - ly be - lieve that you real - ly are here:

Yes, I know that our love is still new, but I
Here in my arms is you be - long.

pro - mise it's gon - na be true. Please let me stay, don't you
How can this feel - ing be wrong? Dar - ling be kind, for I'm

send me a - way, oh, no no.
out of my mind ov - er you. Oh!

Some - thing is burn - ing in - side,_____

Some - thing that can't be de - nied._____

I can't let you out of my sight, dar - ling, love me to -

1.

- night._____

Nice 'n' Easy

Words by Marilyn & Alan Bergman
Music by Lew Spence

Night And Day

Words & Music by Cole Porter

Old Devil Moon

Words by E. Y. Harburg
Music by Burton Lane

On This Night Of A Thousand Stars

Words by Tim Rice
Music by Andrew Lloyd Webber

Verse 2:
In the glow of those twinkling lights,
We shall love through eternity,
On this night in a million nights
Fly away with me.

Paris By Night

Words & Music by Jacques La Rue & M.Phillipe-Gerard
English Adaptation by Jack Fishman

Quiet Nights Of Quiet Stars
(*Corcovado*)

English Words by Gene Lees
Music & Original Words by Antonio Carlos Jobim

Qui - et nights of qui - et stars,

Round Midnight

By Cootie Williams & Thelonious Monk

Moderately slow, in 2

It be-gins to tell 'round mid-night, 'round mid-night.

I do pret-ty well till af-ter sun-down.

Sup-per-time, I'm feel-ing sad. But it

mid - night knows it too. _____ When some

quar - rel we had _____ needs mend - ing, does it

mean that our love _____ is end - ing?

Dar - ling, I need you; late - ly I find _____ you're

out of my arms and I'm out of my mind.

Let our love take wing some mid-night, 'round mid-night.

Let the an-gels sing for your re - turn - ing.

Let our love be safe and sound when old

mid - night comes a - round. ____

rit.

Sexual Healing

Words & Music by Marvin Gaye, Odell Brown & David Ritz

get on the te-le-phone _ and call _____ you up ba - by. And

to - night I know you'll _ be there _____ to re - lieve _ me, but the

To Coda ⊕

love you give to me will breathe. _____

If you don't know _ the thing _ you're deal - ing _____ oh, I _____

2. Get up, get up, get up, get up
    Let's make love tonight
    Wake up, wake up, wake up, wake up
    Cos you do it right
    Baby, I got sick this morning
    A sea was storming inside of me
    Baby, I think I'm capsizing
    The waves are rising and rising
    When I get that feeling I want sexual healing
    Sexual healing is good for me
    Makes me feel so fine, it's such a rush
    Helps to relieve the mind and it's good for us
    Sexual healing, baby, it's good for me
    Sexual healing is something that's good for me.

    That is good for me, that is so good to me
    My baby, oh!
    Come take the crow, just fly me home
    And my body and mind soon will be making it honey
    I'll be feeling fine, you're my medicine
    Open up and let me in
    Darling you're so great
    I can't wait for you to operate.

So Tired

Words & Music by Russ Morgan & Jack Stuart

Moderately slow

all day long I won-der why we're far a-part.

So tired of dream-ing of you, so tired

of wait-ing for you, but tho' I'm tir-ed I'll wait for-ev-er

1. dear. I'm

2. dear.

Stella By Starlight

Music by Victor Young
Words by Ned Washington

Moderately Slow

The Joint Is Jumpin'

Words by Andy Razaf & J.C. Johnson
Music by Thomas Waller

Tempo di-sturb de neighbors

They have a new ex-pres-sion a-long old Har-lem way____ that tells you when a par-ty is ten times more____ than gay.____ To say that things are jump-in' leaves not a sin-gle doubt____ that

The Look Of Love

Words by Hal David
Music by Burt Bacharach

Medium rock ballad

3° instrumental

1. The look _____ of love _____ is in _____ your eyes, _____

(Verse 2 see block lyric)

_____ the look _____ your heart _____ can't dis - guise. _____

The look _____ of love _____

Verse 2:
You've got the look of love, it's on your face,
A look that time can't erase.
Be mine tonight, let this be just the start
Of so many nights like this;
Let's take a lover's vow
And then seal it with a kiss.

I can hardly wait *etc.*

Verse 3: (Instrumental)

I can hardly wait *etc.*

The Nearness Of You

Music by Hoagy Carmichael
Words by Ned Washington

Why do I just with - er and for - get all re - sis - tance when you and your mag - ic pass by? My heart's in a dith - er, dear, when

The Night We Called It A Day

Words by Tom Adair
Music by Matt Dennis

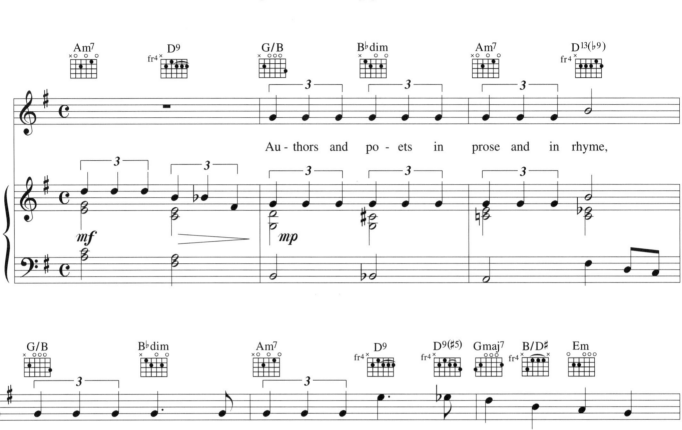

Au - thors and po - ets in prose and in rhyme,

seem to a - gree that night is the time of lov - ers' meet - ings,

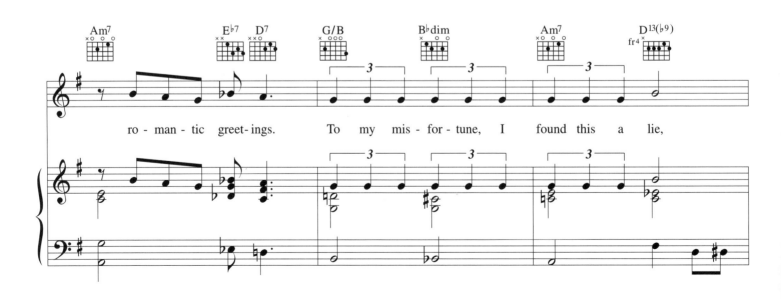

ro - man - tic greet - ings. To my mis - for - tune, I found this a lie,

These Foolish Things

Words by Eric Maschwitz
Music by Jack Strachey

Rather slowly

Oh! will you ne-ver let me be? Oh! will you ne-ver set me free? The ties that bound us are still a-round us, there's no es-cape that I can see. And still those lit-tle things re-

main,

that bring me hap - pi - ness or pain.

Refrain

1. A ci - gar - ette that bears a lip - stick's tra - ces, _____
2. Gar - den - ia per - fume ling - 'ring on a pil - low, _____
3. First daf - fo - dils and long ex - ci - ted ca - bles, _____

an air - line tick - et to ro - man - tic pla - ces. _____
wild straw - b'ries on - ly se - ven francs a ki - lo. _____
and can - dle - light on lit - tle cor - ner ta - bles. _____

And still my heart has wings, _____ these fool - ish
And still my heart has wings, _____ these fool - ish
And still my heart has wings, _____ these fool - ish

things re - mind me of you.
things re - mind me of you.
things re - mind me of you.

A tink - ling pi - a - no in the next a - part - ment, ____
The Park at ev - 'ning when the bell has sound - ed, ____
The smile of Gar - bo and the scent of ro - ses, ____

The Way You Look Tonight

Music by Jerome Kern
Words by Dorothy Fields

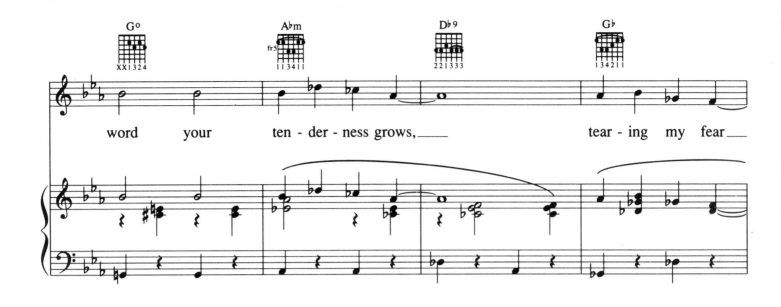

word   your   ten - der - ness grows,____   tear - ing   my   fear____

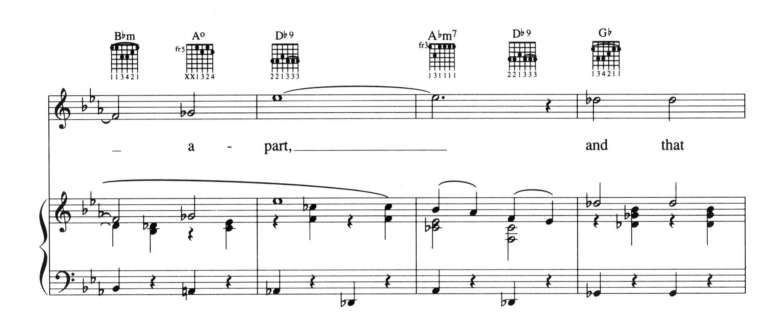

__   a - part,_____   and   that

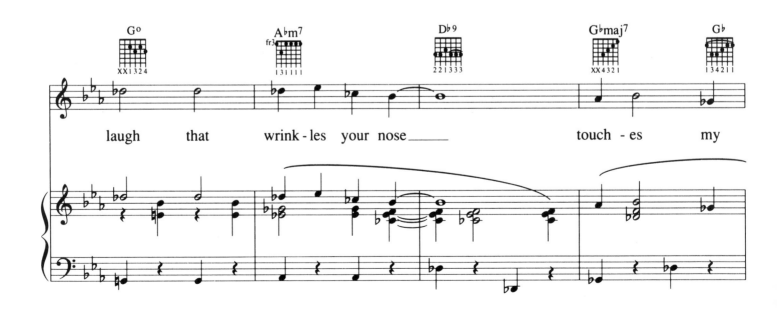

laugh   that   wrink - les   your   nose____   touch - es   my

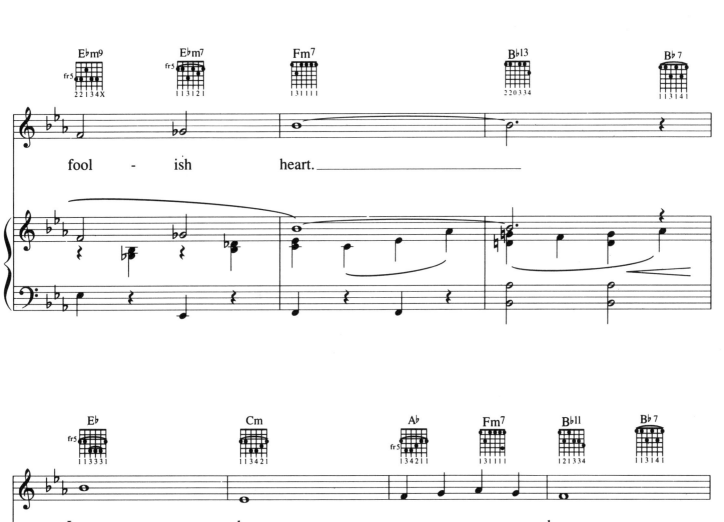

fool - ish heart.

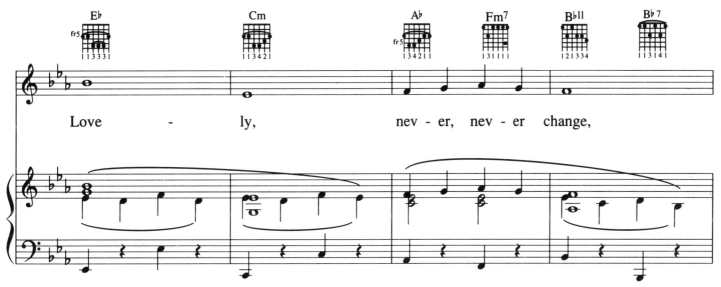

Love - ly, nev - er, nev - er change,

keep that breath-less charm, won't you please ar - range it, 'cause I

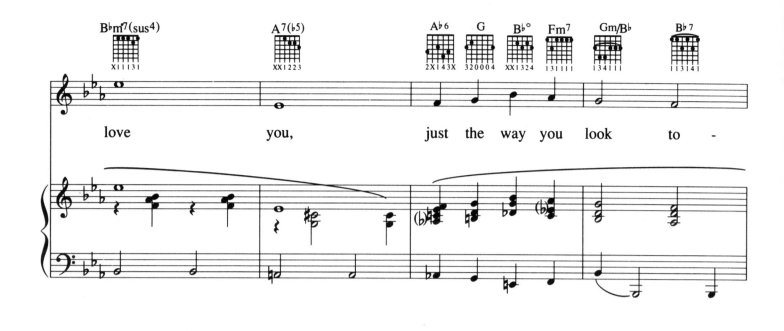

love you, just the way you look to -

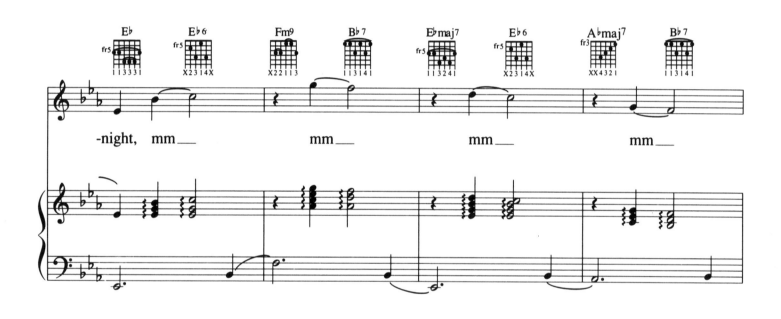

-night, mm___ mm___ mm___ mm___

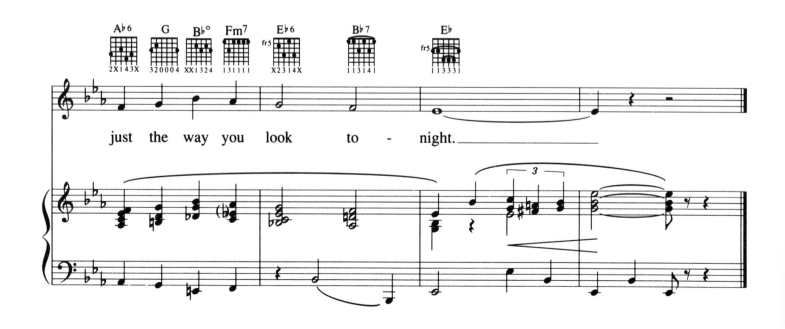

just the way you look to - night._____

Tonight

Music by Leonard Bernstein
Lyrics by Stephen Sondheim

What A Little Moonlight Can Do

Words & Music by Harry Woods

Quick tempo

1. If by chance you are a bash-ful lov-er,_____ don't sit a-round in
2. Na-ture has a fun-ny way a-bout her,_____ of mak-ing peo-ple

deep des-pair._____ On a moon-light night, just
fall in love._____ A night-in-gale to sing, a

Wonderful Tonight

Words & Music by Eric Clapton

Moderately

1. It's late in the eve - ning,
2. We go to a par - ty,
3. It's time to go home __ now,

she's won-d'ring what clothes __ to wear. __
and ev - 'ry-one turns __ to see __
and I've got an ach - ing head. __

She puts on her make-
this beau-ti - ful la -
So I give her the car __

I feel won-der-ful __ be-cause I see __ the love __ light in __ your eyes. Then the won-der of it all __ is that you just don't __ re-a-lise __ how much __ I love __ you.

2/00 (36657)